UNDERSTANDING THE HUMAN BODY
WORKBOOK

UNDERSTANDING THE HUMAN BODY
WORKBOOK

Tove Irene Fjeldstad
Odd Toralf Hushovd
Peter Harrison (Editor)

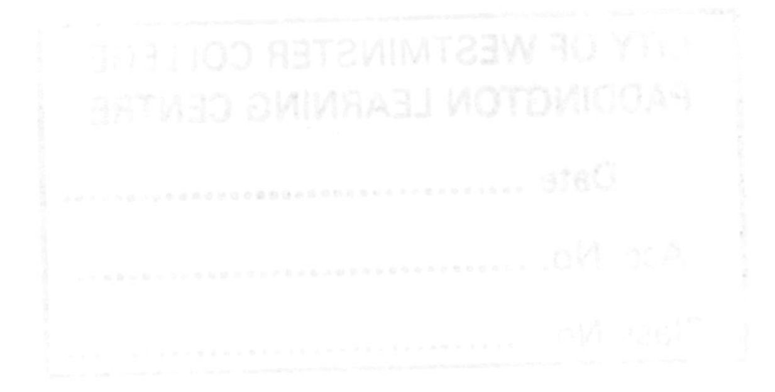

British Library Cataloguing-in-Publication Data
Dietrichs, Espen
Understanding the Human Body – Workbook
I. Title
612

ISBN 1-873732-06-6

Cover and layout:
Ellen Larsen

Illustrations:
K.C. Toverud, P.A. Olsen

Typesetting:
Word Power, Berwickshire

Printed and bound by
The Alden Press, Oxford

384 Lanark Road
Edinburgh EH13 OLX

Contents

Introduction

This workbook has been specifically designed to be used in conjunction with 'Understanding the Human Body'. It can, however, also be used as a practical workbook with other textbooks of human biology.
'Understanding the Human Body' differs from other textbooks in that it does not offer a continuous text with accompanying illustrations. Instead photographs, drawings and texts have been carefully integrated. It is the interaction between illustrations and text which facilitates a complete understanding of how the various organs in our body operate individually and in conjunction with one another. The integrated approach gives the student the opportunity for additional work with the subject matter and this workbook provides exercises and assignments to reinforce and extend the material presented in the textbook.
The assignments have been designed especially to accompany the subject headings in the textbook. They consist of straightforward theoretical questions, exercises to familiarize the student with the names and functions of the various organs, and suggestions for further study. Since they are concerned with authentic medical problems, it is hoped that the relevance of the material will be clear to students.
The work can be undertaken individually or in small groups. The teacher's role as 'supervisor' is important in order to ensure that the answers are correct. Blank pages are provided, where appropriate, for answering the questions.
It is important that students not only find answers to the questions, but also practise formulating comments and making connections themselves. The marked assignments(*) do not have answers which can simply be found in the relevant chapter of the textbook. Students will need to consult other chapters of the textbook or refer to appropriate supplementary literature.
Additional assignments have been included in the back of the book which assume an awareness of the relationship between the various body systems.
Suggestions for alterations or improvements as well as general comments will be much appreciated.

The cell

1 What are the characteristic features of living cells?

2 A skin cell is 0.001 mm long and 0.01 mm wide. Calculate how many cells there are on 1 mm^2 of your skin.

3 Assignment
Study slipper animalcule under a microscope.

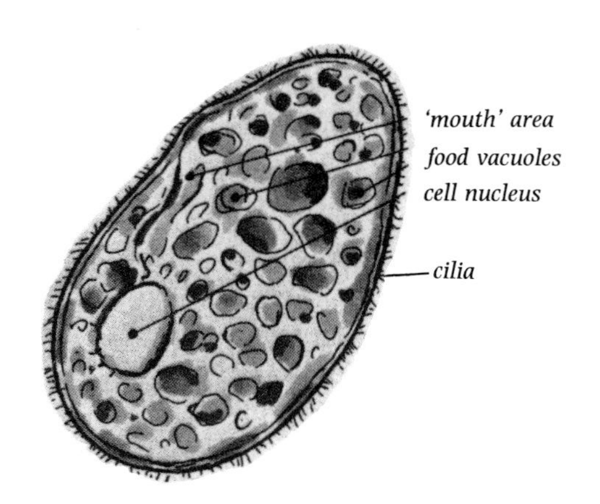

Slipper animalcules are single-celled organisms. They can be obtained by creating a hay culture. Place some grass or hay at the bottom of a glass jar. Fill the jar approximately half full of water (preferably from a stagnant pool).
Put on a lid and leave the jar alone for one to two weeks. A film will form on the surface of the water and this film will contain slipper animalcules.

Using a pipette, suck up a drop of fluid. Transfer this on to a slide. Put a cover glass over the drop and look at the specimen under the microscope (first using a small magnification). To make the creatures swim more slowly, an agar solution of 2% or a weak starch solution can be added to the slide. Using the microscope, it is now possible to observe how these single-celled organisms are capable of moving about. We can observe how they respond to their surroundings.
Note how they will try to swim away from the strong light of the microscope. We see how they pump out surplus water (pulsating follicles) and how they absorb nutrients. (When a little carmine is added, you can, if you are lucky, observe the creatures absorbing small red grains into the the cytoplasm). Seeing absorption of nutrients can be difficult. The nutrients (a microbe, for example) are hurled toward a chasm, the 'mouth', on the surface. There, the whole microbe is absorbed and subsequently digested within the cell. The exchange of oxygen (O_2) and carbon dioxide (CO_2) takes place by diffusion through the cell membrane.

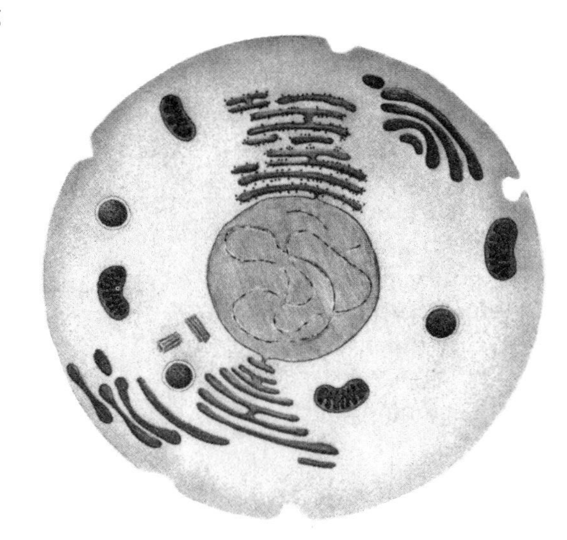

4 Study the diagram of a cross-section of a cell.
Identify and name the various parts. (Did you spot all the parts in the slipper animalcule?) Can you explain why all the small parts of a cell do not become visible under a light microscope?

5 Assignment
Observing cells under a microscope.

Cheek cells (epithelium cells on the inside cheek) can be scraped off with a wooden spatula. Rub the tip of the spatula through a drop of iodine solution or methyl blue on a slide and look at the cells under a microscope. Make a sketch and add names to the parts that you observe.
Onion cells can be studied under a microscope by pulling the onion membrane from the inside of an onion skin. Place a piece of membrane in a drop of methyl blue, water or iodine solution and watch the cells under a microscope. Make a sketch and name the parts.

Can you see the differences between vegetable and animal cells?

6 Fill in the following table with keywords and their specific functions.

PART OF CELL	FUNCTION
cell membrane	
cell nucleus	
cytoplasmic reticular	
mitochondrion	
ribosome	
chromosome	

7 How does transportation into and out of cells occur?

8 What is combustion?

9 Why does a cell need energy?

10 Which nutrients does a cell use to produce energy?

11 Which characteristic features should all living cells have in common? (see assignment 1).

12 All cells contain hereditary material (DNA). Where is DNA located within the cell?

13 How are proteins made up? Why are proteins such important substances within the cells? Name some examples of important tasks performed by proteins within the body.

14 The hereditary material instructs the cells as to which type of protein is to be made. Briefly explain how this happens within the cells.

Chromosomes and cell division

1 What is a chromosome?

2 How many chromosomes do the following human cells contain?

a brain cells

b muscle cells

c skin cells

d liver cells

3 What is a gene?

4 What is the most important aspect of an ordinary cell division (mitosis)?

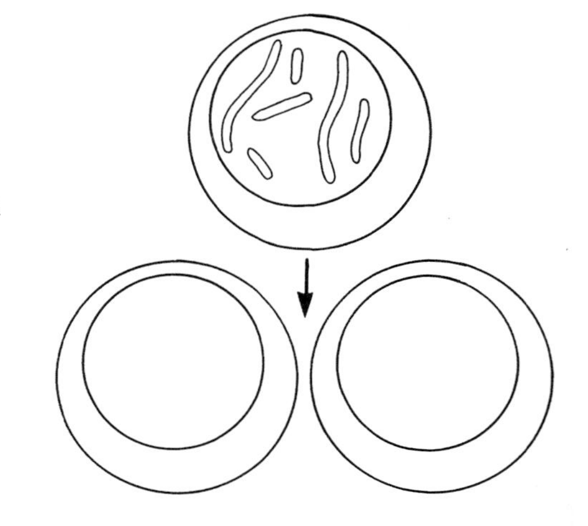

5 Look at the figure and answer the following questions.

a How many chromosomes are there in this cell?

b How many chromosome pairs are there in this cell?

c How many chromosomes will each new cell contain after the cell has divided itself through mitosis?
Draw the chromosomes in each of the new cells in the illustration.

6 a How many chromosomes are there in the cell?

b How many pairs of chromosome are there?

c Explain why there are double chromosomes.
Draw the chromosomes contained within each new cell.

7 Where is the hereditary material to be found which determines the sex characteristic?

***8** What is the name of the chemical combination that makes up the hereditary material?

Tissue

1 What is tissue?

2 List the various types of tissue found in the human body. List the main functions of each type of tissue.

3 What is skin tissue and where can it be found?

4 Certain kinds of epithelium consist of one layer, others of several layers. How does the composition of epithelium relate to its particular function? Give specific examples.

5 What is glandular tissue and where is it found in the human body?

6 Which types of connective and supporting tissue are there in the human body?

*7 What kind of tissue constitutes the lining of the windpipe?

*8 List the main differences between the various types of muscular tissue.

9 What is lymph?

10 Assignment

Study specimens of human tissue under the microscope. Make a sketch of what you see and compare this to the diagrams shown in the textbook.

Blood circulation and blood vessels

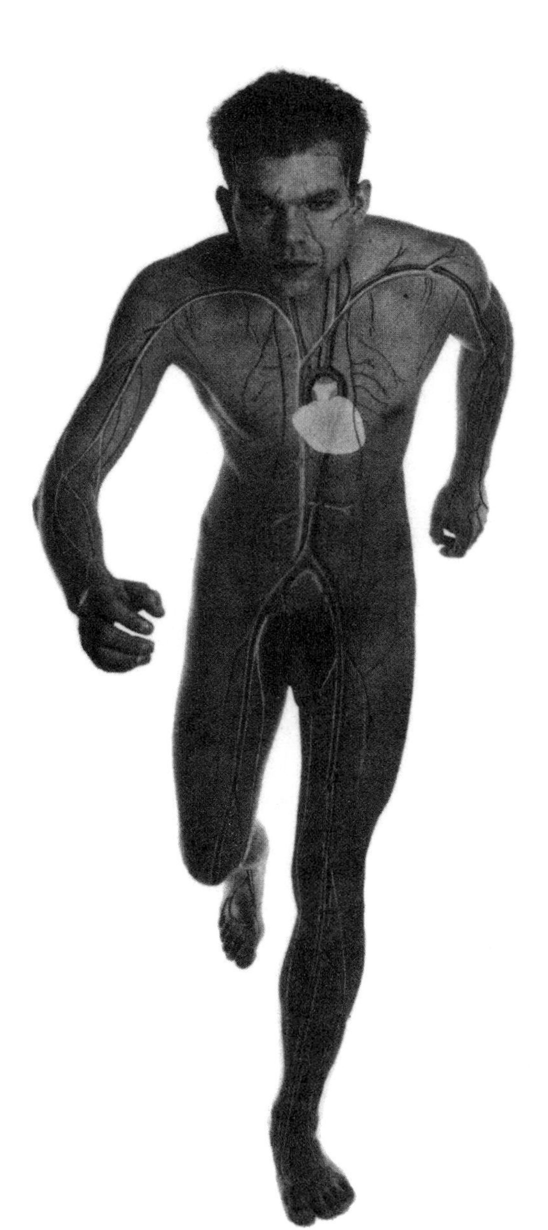

1 What are the most essential aspects of blood circulation?

2 Name the substances transported in the blood.

3 Write down the names of the organs that form part of the circulation system. Why are some blood vessels illustrated as red and others blue in the textbook.
Name the largest arteries and vessels in the body.

The Blood Vessels

4 There are three types of blood vessels: arteries, capillaries and veins.

a What structural differences are there between these threetypes of blood vessels?

b What is the relationship between their structure and their function.

c What is the blood pressure in
  i arteries
  ii capillaries
  iii veins?

d Why does the human body have such a large amount of capillaries?

5 The body has two distinct circulation systems, these being the lesser and greater systems. The heart is the common pump of both systems.

a The lesser circulation system
  i Draw a simplified diagram illustrating the flow of blood in the lesser circulation system.
  ii What is the function of the lesser circulation system? What is so special about the arteries in the lungs?

b The greater circulation system
  i Draw a simplified diagram illustrating the flow of blood in the greater circulation system.
  ii What happens to the blood in the greater circulation system?

6 Assuming an average adult has five litres of blood:

a What volume of blood is in the greater circulation system?

b What volume of blood is in the lesser circulation system?

7 Assignment
Sit on a chair and raise one arm, allowing the other to hang down limply by your side. Continue this for two minutes and in the meantime note how it feels. Next place your hands side by side on the table and compare them. Discuss what has happened to the blood flow in each of the arms. Can you give reasons for this?

8 a What are varicose veins?

b How and where do they usually occur?

c What can be done to prevent varicose veins?

9 a What is meant by hardening of the arteries?

b What are the causes of hardening of the arteries?

c What effect do eating habits have on hardening of the arteries?

d What effect does nicotine have on hardening of the arteries?

e What can you do to avoid hardening of the arteries?

The heart

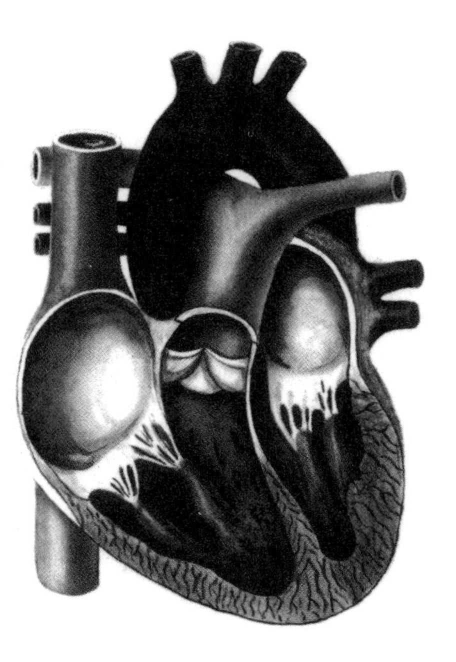

1 What is the primary task of the heart?

2 Draw a diagram showing the structure of the heart and name the various parts.

***3** What are the special features of cardiac muscle tissue when compared to skeleton muscle tissue?

4 How does the heart itself obtain oxygen and nutrients for muscular activity?

5 a Which mechanisms in the heart ensure that the blood does not flow in the wrong direction?

b Explain the bloodflow through the heart.

6 How many times a minute does the heart normally contract when at rest?

7 How much blood does the heart pump out per minute
a at rest

b during moderate activity

c at maximal effort?

8 What is the specific name given to this blood volume per minute?

9 What happens to the heart when the body needs more oxygen, for instance in case of physical effort?

10 What is an ECG and what is its purpose?

11 Assignment
Study and discuss, for example, a pig's heart. Try to find the various structures and study the arteries and veins running from and toward the heart.

12 In what way would you offer first aid in case of a cardiac arrest.

13 a What is angina pectoris?

b What is a cardiac infarct?

14 What is blood pressure?

15 a What is systolic blood pressure?

b What is diastolic blood pressure?

16 Explain the principles of blood pressure measuring and why this procedure is carried out so frequently in a hospital situation.

17 What is normal blood pressure for a fit young person?

18 Why does blood pressure rise with age?

*19 Mention other causes of high blood pressure.

*20 What can sustained high blood pressure lead to when left untreated?

*21 What can be done to prevent high blood pressure?

*22 What happens to a person's blood pressure in the case of a shock or loss of blood? What first aid is given in such situations?

*23 Explain why blood pressure is not the same in all arteries.

24 a What is a pulse wave?

b Where can the pulse wave be felt best?

c For how long does the pulse have to be taken (the principle of pulse beat counting)?

d Why should the thumb not be used for taking the pulse?

25 **Assignment**
Find your own pulse beat or that of a fellow student at the wrist or at the carotid artery. Count the beats while you time 15 seconds. Practise this a few times.
Your heart beat per minute is the count during 15 seconds multiplied by 4.
Use a stethoscope on a fellow student and listen. What do you hear? Can you identify the two heart sounds? What causes these two sounds?

26 **Assignment**
Requirements: sphygmanometer, stethoscope, thermometer, gauze or cotton wool, adhesive tape.

The experiment is designed to study what happens to pulse and blood pressure following a bout of physical effort. The class divides itself into groups of at least three people. Each group consists of one subject and two people who collect the data.

a *Physical effort*

Measure the blood pressure and pulse of the subject at rest. Record the values in the chart below. The subject then has to walk up and down a flight of stairs for three minutes or do twenty press ups. Allow the subject to start slowly with subsequent acceleration. (Why is a slow start necessary?) Measure blood pressure and pulse immediately after the activity. Record the values on the chart. Next, measure every minute for 5 minutes and record the values. How long does it take before pulse and blood pressure return to the rates recorded before expending physical effort?

		Blood Pressure	Pulse
Before physical effort	at rest		
Time after physical effort (minutes)	0		
	1		
	2		
	3		
	4		
	5		
	6		

The blood

1 What are the functions of blood?

2 What does blood consist of? Make a list of the components.

3 Describe the functions of:

a red blood corpuscles

b white blood corpuscles

c blood platelets

4 What is the difference in structure between red and white blood corpuscles?

5 Assignment
Look at specimens of blood corpuscles under the microscope and draw red and white blood corpuscles. Do you find different types of white corpuscles?

6 What is haemoglobin and what is its function?

7 What is anaemia?

* **8** Athletes often train at high altitudes.
Try to explain why they do this.

9 What is meant by blood acting as a buffer? What constituents within the blood allow it to do this?

10 Where in the body are blood corpuscles produced?

11 Write brief notes on:

a the gases which are dissolved in blood

b waste matter in blood

c ions (electrolytes) in blood

12 a What are blood groups?

b Which blood groups can you name?

c Why is it dangerous to give a blood transfusion from a person with blood group B to a person with blood group A?

The lymphatic system

1 What are the main tasks of the lymphatic system?

2 a What are lymph nodes?

b Where in the body can they be found and what is their function?

3 What is the function of the spleen?

4 When a cancer is removed in a surgical operation the lymph nodes near it are removed as well. What is the reason for this?

5 What is an antigen? Mention some examples of antigens.

6 a What are antibodies?

b Where can antibodies be formed?

c How do they work?

7 How does the body's defence mechanism combat an infection?

8 What does it mean when someone has become immune to a disease?

9 a What is vaccination?

b What does vaccination entail?

c Against which diseases are people usually vaccinated?

d Which infectious diseases can vaccination not prevent?

10 What is AIDS? Try to find material about this disease ie. how it is caused and how it is transmitted to others.

11 a What is an allergy?

b Which symptoms usually indicate an allergic reaction?

c What can be the cause of allergic reactions?

d How can an allergy be treated?

The respiratory system

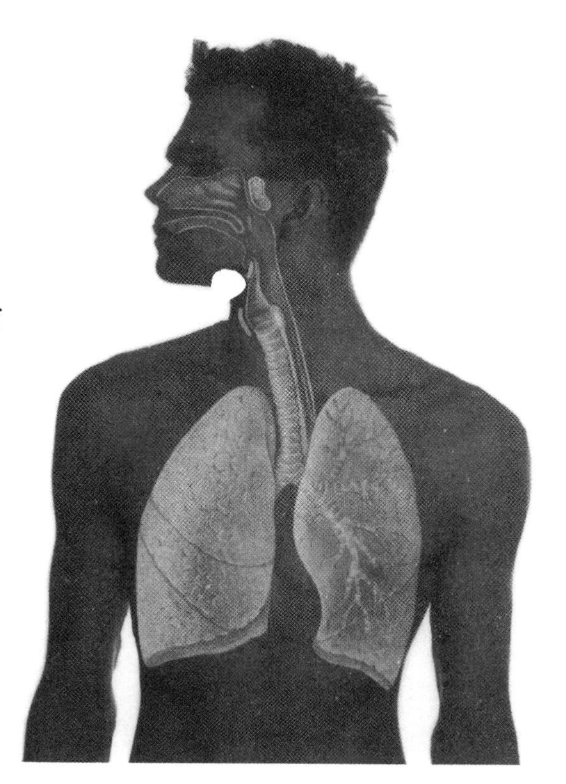

1 What are the main functions of the respiratory system?

2 Using the illustration name the organs of the respiratory system.

3 Explain the mechanics of how air is passed into and out of the body (inhalation and exhalation).

4 a How is the windpipe positioned in relation to the oesophagus?

b Which types of tissue make up the windpipe?

c Which mechanism prevents food and drink from entering the windpipe?

5 What protects the lungs inside the chest cavity?

6 a How are the lungs kept inflated?

b What happens when the pulmonary membrane is punctured?

7 What is the main difference between inhaled and exhaled air?

8 Explain how gas exchange occurs in the alveoli.

9 a What is asthma?

b What is meant by bronchial infections?

10 Assignment
Requirements: plastic bags with a minimum volume of 5 litres.
Relax for a moment and inhale and exhale quietly. Count the number of times you breathe in the course of one minute. Then walk up and down some stairs for a few minutes, or do some press ups. Sit down

and once again count the number of times you breathe per minute. Do you notice a difference? Explain why the breathing frequency has altered.
Sit still and quietly breathe in and out. Breathe out into an empty plastic bag. Make sure that you don't allow any extra air to enter the bag. Only the air that you exhale should go into the bag. The volume of air you exhale into the bag is called the normal breathing volume. What was it in your case? Try to measure it.
Afterwards breathe the air that is left in your lungs after a normal exhalation into an empty plastic bag. How much air is there in the bag? This volume is called the reserve volume.
Finally inhale as deeply as possible and exhale as much as you can into the bag.
How much air is there? This volume is called the vital capacity.
Compare and discuss the results.

Speech and breathing

1 Explain how air enters and leaves the lungs.

2 **Assignment**
Cross your arms over your chest, with your hands flat on either side of it. In this position you can check the movements of the ribs. Hold on tight and breathe in. What is moving now?

3 a What function does coughing serve?

b What must you to do to avoid spreading infection when coughing?

4 a Where are the vocal cords located?

b How is sound produced with the vocal cords?

5 What social function does the production of sound have?

6 Which organs, in addition to the vocal cords, are important for the power of speech?

7 Where in the brain is the speech centre?

Sensory nerve endings and nerve cells

1 What is a sensory organ?

2 What senses do human beings possess?

3 Which types of senses are stimulated when you:

a move a hair on your arm

b cut your finger

c get dressed

d read

e eat toffee

f go to a disco?

4 Do you think there are any benefits in having sense organs which are sensitive to pain?

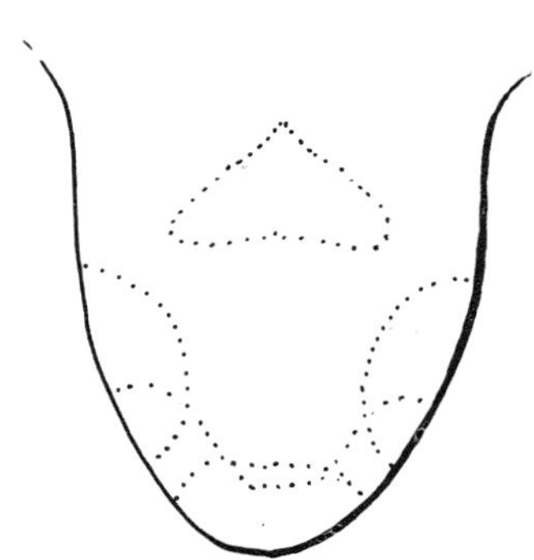

5 Assignment
Which tastes can you distinguish and where are the various taste buds?

Requirements: cotton buds and the following solutions:

10% NaCl (kitchen salt)	– salt
15% sugar solution	– sweet
0.1% HCL	– sour
0.02% cyanide sulphate solution	– bitter

Two students work together. One student sticks out his tongue and the other rubs a cotton bud dipped into the sugar solution over the protruding tongue. Indicate on the illustration where the subject experiences the sweet taste. The subject rinses the mouth and dries the tongue before sampling the next solution. Repeat for the other solutions and indicate again on the illustration the areas on the tongue where each taste is experienced most strongly.
Compare notes in class.

6 What are the functions of nerve cells?

7 Using the illustration opposite, add names to the various parts. Outline the direction of the nerve impulse along the nerve cell.

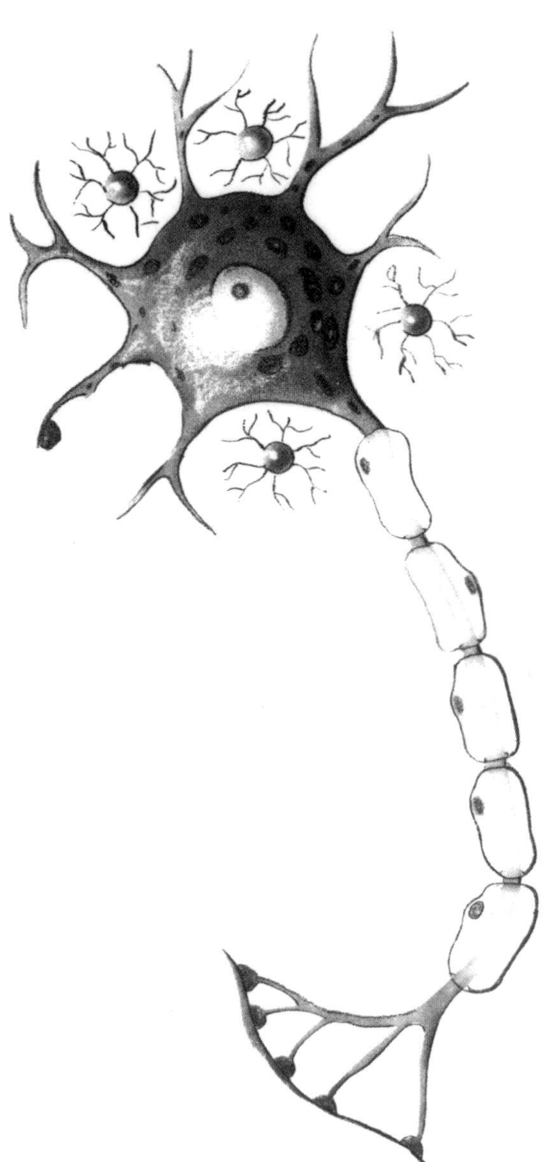

8 What is a:

a nerve cell

b nerve

c myelin sheath

d synapse?

9 How does a nerve impulse travel from nerve cell to nerve cell?

10 Assignment

The impulse conduction by the nervous system can be illustrated in the following manner. The whole class sits in a circle facing outwards. The students hold each other's hands. Two students share a stopwatch between them so that both can operate it. One of these students starts the impulse by pressing his/her neighbour's hand and simultaneously starting the stopwatch. When the neighbour feels the pressure, he/she passes on the incoming impulse by pressing his/her neighbour's hand, etc. Thus it goes full circle until the last person on feeling the pressure, presses the stopwatch. (Why should students always sit facing outwards?)

You can now calculate how much time passes between the moment someone feels the pressure and passes it on. This can be done as follows:

reaction time: $\frac{t}{N-1}$ (t=measured time and n=number of students)

There should first be a few trials to practise. Then do three tests and record the results.

The nervous system

1 What are the differences between the central nervous system and the peripheral nervous system?

2 What is a reflex? Give some examples of reflexes.

3 Assignment
An example of a reflex is the knee jerk reflex. This reflex is often tested during a physical examination. The test is performed to investigate whether there is anything wrong with the functioning of the nervous system, because some diseases can cause the absence of certain reflexes.

Sit on a table with legs dangling straight down. A fellow student gently taps the tendon just below the kneecap with a small hammer. You should now experience a knee jerk reflex. Sometimes it can be difficult to tap the right spot so you may need to try it a few times. Explain what happens.

4 The nervous system can also be divided into a voluntary and an involuntary part. What is the main difference between the two?

5 Which of the following responses are controlled by the voluntary nervous system?

a Secretion of hormones by/from the glands

b Changes in heart frequency (pulse rate)

c Contraction of muscles in the arms

d Contraction of muscles in the intestinal tract

6 The involuntary nervous system is further divided into a sympathetic and parasympathetic part. On the chart on page 40 record which functions are controlled by the sympathetic system and which functions are controlled by the parasympathetic system.

	Sympathetic stimulation	Parasympathetic stimulation
Faster heart beat		
Higher blood pressure		
Increased perspiration		
Decreased bowel activity		
Increased bowel activity		
Lower blood pressure		
Slower heart beating		
Widening of the bronchi in the lungs		
Contracting of blood vessels in the skin		
Increase in blood supply to muscles		
Widening of the pupils		

7 Which part of the involuntary nervous system operates primarily, when:

a you relax after a good meal?

b you get very angry?

Explain your answers.

8 What is the vagus nerve?

9 What is the difference between sensory and motor nerve fibres?

10 What are the main functions of the spinal cord?

11 What is the difference between the grey and white matter in the brain? Where are these areas located?
Label the various parts of the brain and spinal cord.

12 Describe the main functions of the various parts of the central nervous system.

13 Name the membranes that surround the brain/spinal cord. What functions do they perform?

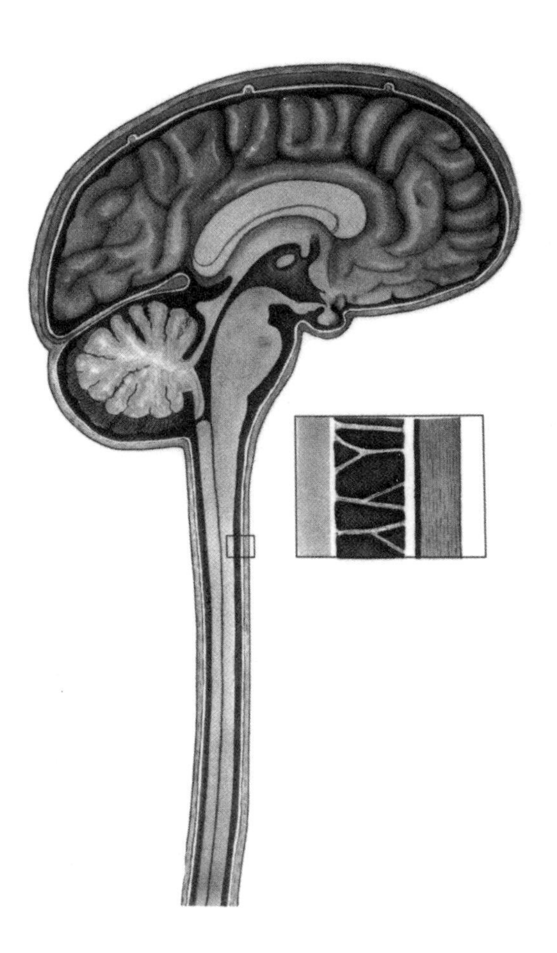

14 a What is cerebro-spinal fluid?

b Where can this fluid be found and what is its function?

c How can the pressure of this fluid remain constant when new fluid is constantly being produced?

15 Which part of the brain is deficient if a patient requires artificial respiration after a stroke?

***16** The ability to learn is linked with specific areas of the cerebral cortex. How do we know this?

17 What happens when the visual cortex or the centre of hearing in the brain is damaged or destroyed?

18 What are the important differences between the left and the right hemispheres of the brain?

19 People's behaviour when under the influence of alcohol varies. On the basis of your own observations of people who were drunk, can you say which parts of the brain no longer operate properly as a result of an excess of alcohol?

20 When parts of the cerebellum have been destroyed, what effect does this have on a persons ability to perform motor skills?

***21** What effect do the following diseases have on the central nervous system:

a cerebral paresis

b Parkinson's disease

c epilepsy

d poliomyelitis

e MS (multiple sclerosis)?

22 Strokes which affect the left hemisphere of the brain often lead to speech impediments. Similar injuries to the right hemisphere do not impair the power of speech. Why is this?

***23** The human brain is much bigger than that of an animal. How does this fact correspond with what you know about the differences between animals and humans?

Hearing and balance

1 Label the parts of the ear using the illustration.

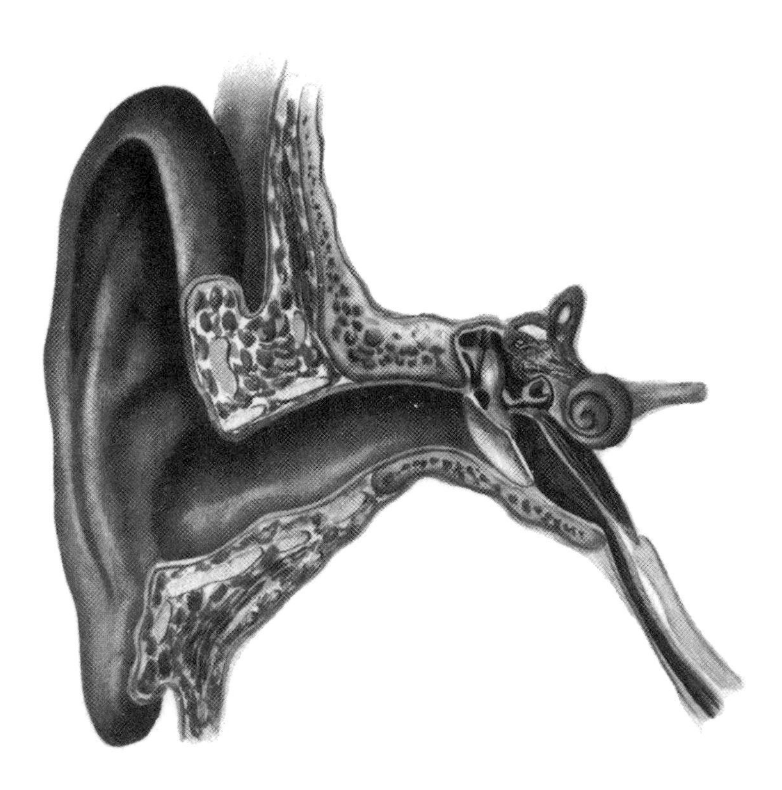

2 What is the function of the ear cartilage of the outer ear?

* **3** Wax is secreted from the auditory canal. Does earwax have a function?

4 What is the function of the eardrum?

5 What is the function of the ossicles?

6 a Where are the hearing cells and what function do they have?

b Where exactly does the perception of sound occur?

c How can we distinguish between high and low tones?

d Explain what might happen if you were to be exposed to a very loud noise for a long period of time.

* **7** Why is chewing gum or yawning helpful when you land or take off in an aeroplane?

8 A cold or sore throat can often lead to inflammation of the middle ear. Why?

9 Assignment

Location of sound.

The subject sits blindfolded on a chair. Use a clock with a loud tick and hold it to the right, behind and in front of the subject's head in that order.

Ensure that the distance from the ears is always the same. Ask the subject to indicate the direction of the sound source. Repeat the test, but now keeping the clock to one side of the subject. What can you conclude?

***10** Which frequencies can be heard by animals?

11 a Where are the semi-circular canals located and what is their function?

b Why do we need three semi-circular canals, rather than only one?

c Explain how the sensory cells operate in the semi-circular canals.

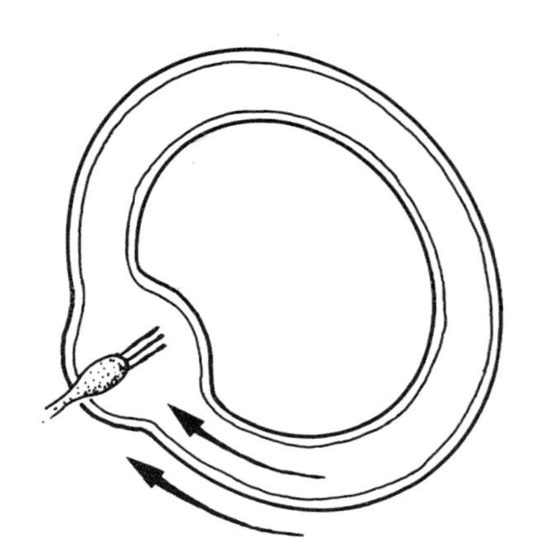

12 The illustration shows a semi-circular canal. The semi-circular canal and the fluid inside it move at the same speed. If a dancer performs a pirouette:

a In which direction are the hair-like receptors bent when the dancer suddenly stops?

b What do you think the dancer feels when he/she stops suddenly?

c Try it yourself and spin around quickly a few times. Describe what you feel and explain what happens.

13 Which senses are used for keeping one's balance? Stand with feet next to each other and arms outstretched sideways. Ask a partner to check whether you stand quite still. Repeat this test, but with your eyes closed. Do you notice any difference?

Sight

1 Look at your neighbour's eyes and at a model of an eye and identify the following parts:

a eyebrow

b lashes

c sclera

d iris

e cornea

f pupil

What functions do each of the above perform?

2 a Label the various parts of the eye shown in the illustration.

b Below are some definitions. Indicate by using the relevant letter which definitions relate to the names which you labelled in the illlustration.

A: space filled with fluid
B: space filled with a kind of jelly
C: the largest part of the light refraction takes place here
D: the light goes straight through here
E: white of the eye
F: can change form and alter the refraction of light
G: membrane without blood vessels
H: here we almost exclusively find cones
I: here we find mostly rods
J: muscles which can change the form of the lens
K: is a cranial nerve

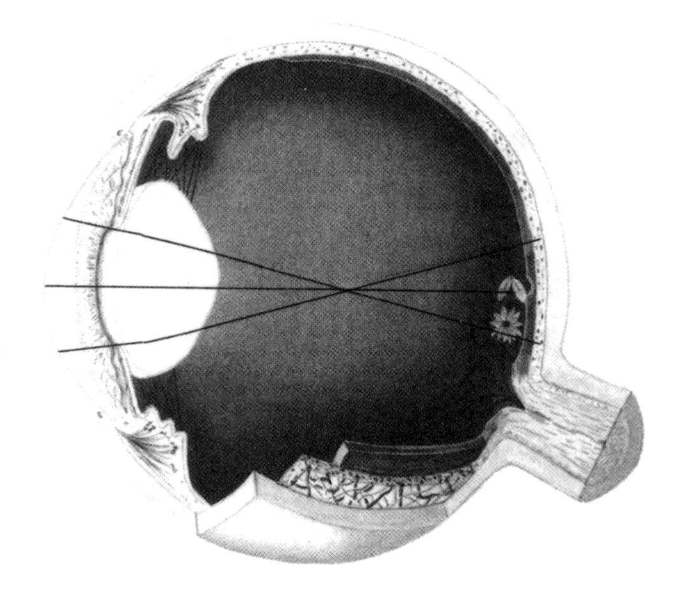

3 Look at your hands, holding them at arm's length from your eyes. Focus on your fingers. What happens to the surrounding area? Focus on this area. How clear are your fingers now? Explain what happens and how the eyes manage to do this.

4 What is the blind spot? Keep a hand in front of your right eye. Look at the plus sign in the illustration. Start by holding the page as close as possible. Slowly move the illustration away from you. At a certain moment the circle will vanish, but the square remains. Explain this.

5 What is the macula?

6 Study the pupil in different light conditions by using a torch. What happens to its shape? What causes this change to occur?

7 When you enter a dark room having come from the sunshine, you cannot see much initially. Gradually things become clear. Explain this phenomenon.

* 8 Is there anyone in class who is short-sighted or long-sighted? Make a sketch and illustrate how the glasses worn by these students contribute toward them being able to focus clearly on objects.

9 Which sensory cells are responsible for colour perception? Where are these cells located?

10 **Assignment**
Requirements: a dark room with light that can be dimmed.

Put some coloured pieces of paper on the table (blue, green, yellow and red). Switch off the light and wait a moment. Gradually increase the light intensity. Which piece of coloured paper do you see first? What does this tell you about eyesight? Which colour would you choose for your car when road safety is your main concern? Explain your answer.

11 What does colour-blindness mean?

12 a What is night-blindness?

b What can night-blindness be attributed to?

13 Man has depth sensitivity (stereoscopic sight). What is this and what are its benefits? Test depth sensitivity: close one eye, stretch your arms and in a quick movement bring your fingertips together. Try this again with both eyes open. What difference do you notice?

*14 Where do the images that one sees actually arise?

15 a What is glaucoma?

b What are cataracts?

*16 Why do most people need reading glasses as they get older?

Hormones

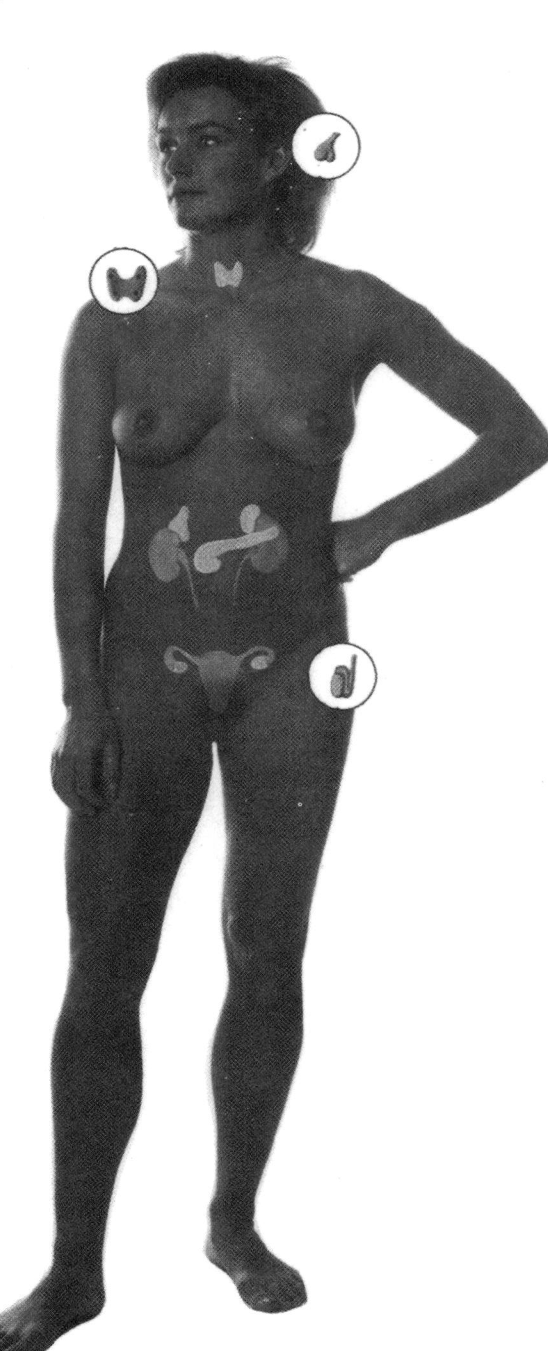

1 What is the difference between internal secretion glands and other glands?

2 What is a hormone?

3 a What is a receptor?

b Explain how a receptor functions.

c Do you find the same receptors everywhere in the body?

4 List five physiological activities which are regulated by hormones.

5 Usually hormones are quickly broken down and distributed. Why is this necessary?

6 Explain what is meant by feedback control of the hormone quantities in the body.

7 Add names to the hormone producing organs in the illustration. List the names of the hormones which are produced by these organs and briefly describe their effect on body functions.

8 a What are the functions of the pituitary gland?

b What would happen to bodily functions if the pituitary gland stopped operating?

9 What is diabetes?

10 How is the sugar level in the blood controlled?

11 What happens to hormone production in the body if:

* a you don't get enough iodine in your food

b you eat too much sugar

c you are startled by a loud noise

d you breastfeed a child

e you drink too much beer?

The digestive system

1 What are the main functions of the digestive tract?

2 a What are the most important nutrients in food?

b What should the nutrient pattern be like in a well constituted diet?

3 Explain why you may not have a balanced diet even though you consume large quantities of food.

4 Under normal conditions, the consumption of 10 kilos of food produces a weight increase of 1 kilo. Explain what happens with the other 9 kilos of food.

5 Label the organs of the digestive tract in the illustration. Use a model as well and look for the various organs.

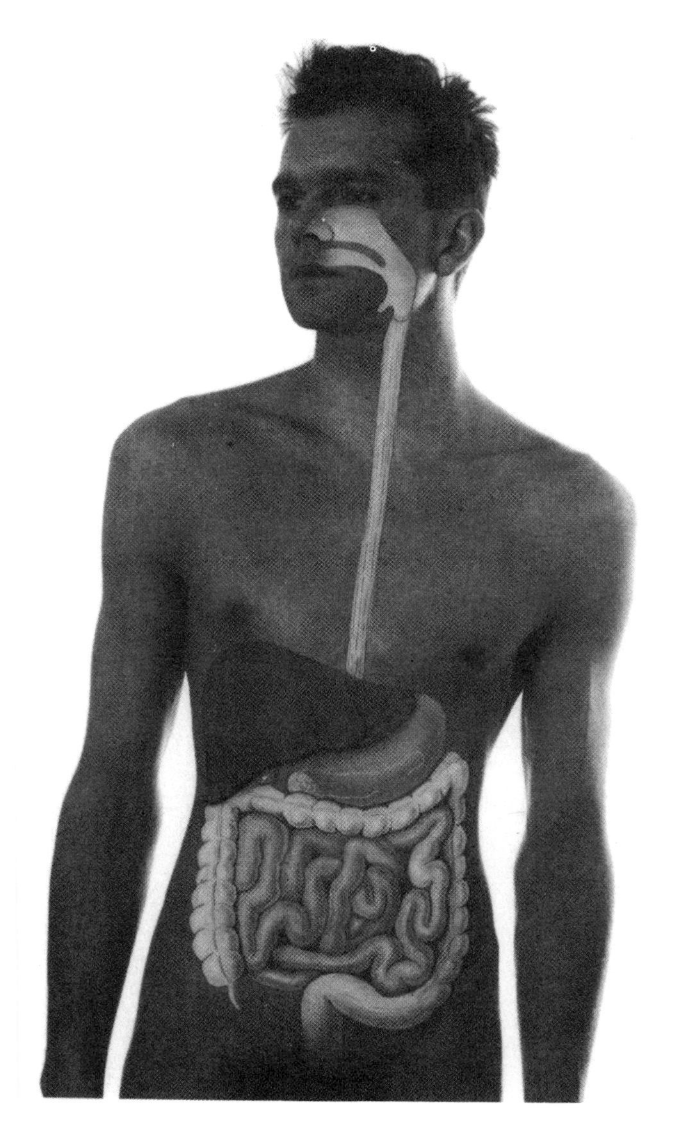

6 What are the functions of saliva? What does saliva contain and where is it produced?

7 a What are the functions of the teeth?

b Label the diagram illustrated on the right.

c How many teeth does an adult have?

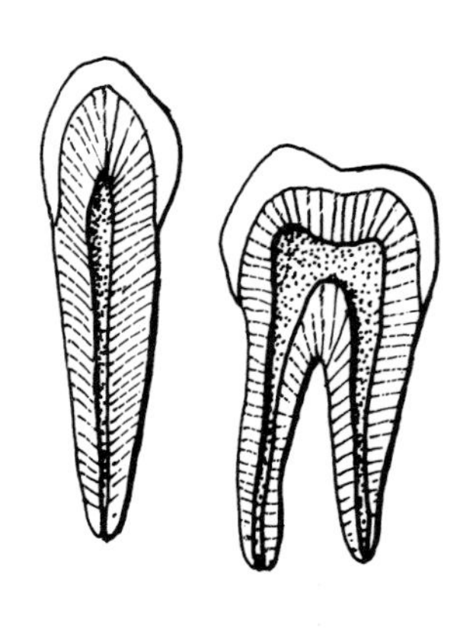

8 What are the functions of the tongue?

9 In the chart below, indicate what substances are found to help digest food in the:

palate	
pharynx	
gullet	
stomach	

10 It is possible to eat while standing on one's head (although not recommended). Explain how food is transported through the digestive tract.

11 The digestive tract is lined with mucous membrane. What is its structure?

12 What is an enzyme?

13 What are the functions of the gastric juice? Why does it not usually break down the lining of the stomach wall?

14 Once the food reaches the small intestine, further digestion depends on the addition of enzymes produced in the liver and the pancreas. Name these enzymes and their functions.

15 Use various colours to indicate in the following illustration where fats, carbohydrates and proteins are decomposed in the digestive tract. Indicate briefly where the various enzymes are produced within the body.

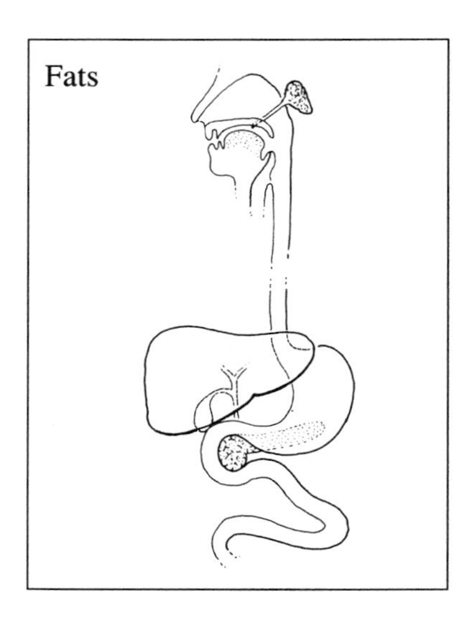

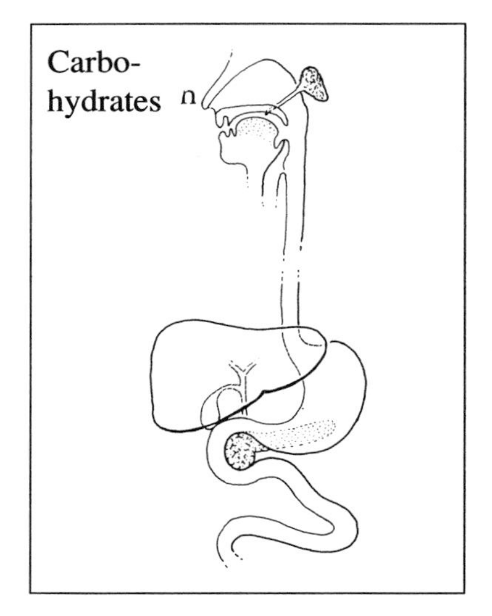

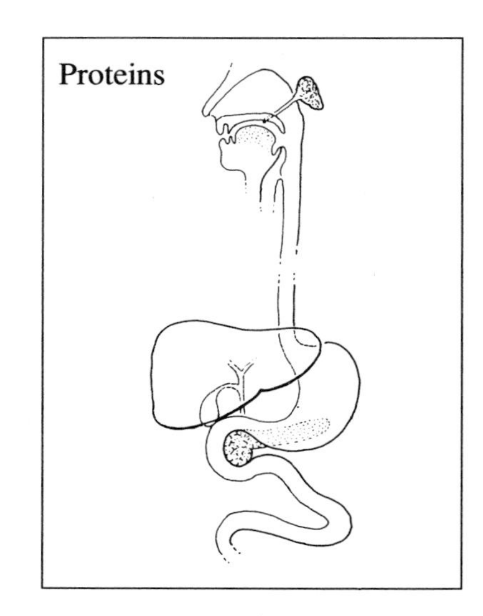

16 What are the following nutrients broken down into within the digestive tract?

a Fats

b Carbohydrates

c Proteins

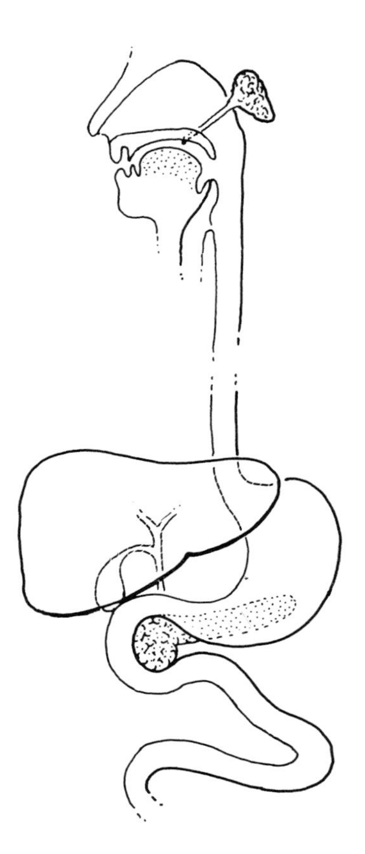

17 The inside of the small intestine has folds and contains numerous intestinal villi. The epithelial cells in the mucous membrane contain many minute projections (microvilli).
What digestive function do these structures perform?

18 The absorption of nutrients takes place in the small intestine. Where do these fats go after being broken down and what happens to the other nutrients?

19 What is the portal vein and what is its function?

20 List the functions of the liver.

21 What digestive function is performed by the large intestine?

22 Why can chronic and serious diarrhoea be life-threatening?

23 a Why is fibre beneficial to your health?

b List foods that are high in fibre content.

***24** Vitamin K is absorbed in the large intestine.
Where does this vitamin originate and what function does it serve within the human body?

25 What is the composition of faeces?

***26** What regulates the emptying of the bowels?

27 Assignment

The operation of enzymes in the stomach.

Prepare three solutions, A, B and C in three separate beakers.
Solution A: 2 ml 10 % HCl, 0.5 g pepsin and 100 ml water
Solution B: 2 ml 10% HCl and 100 ml of water
Solution C: 0.5 g pepsin in 100 ml of water.

Some boiled protein is placed into three test tubes, marked A, B and C. The three solutions are each poured into a test tube. Cover the test tubes and place them in an incubator (37° C) until the next day. (Allow some extra time if the test tubes are kept at room temperature). Describe and explain the results.

The urinary system

1 What are the main functions of the urinary system?

2 Label the various parts of the urinary system.

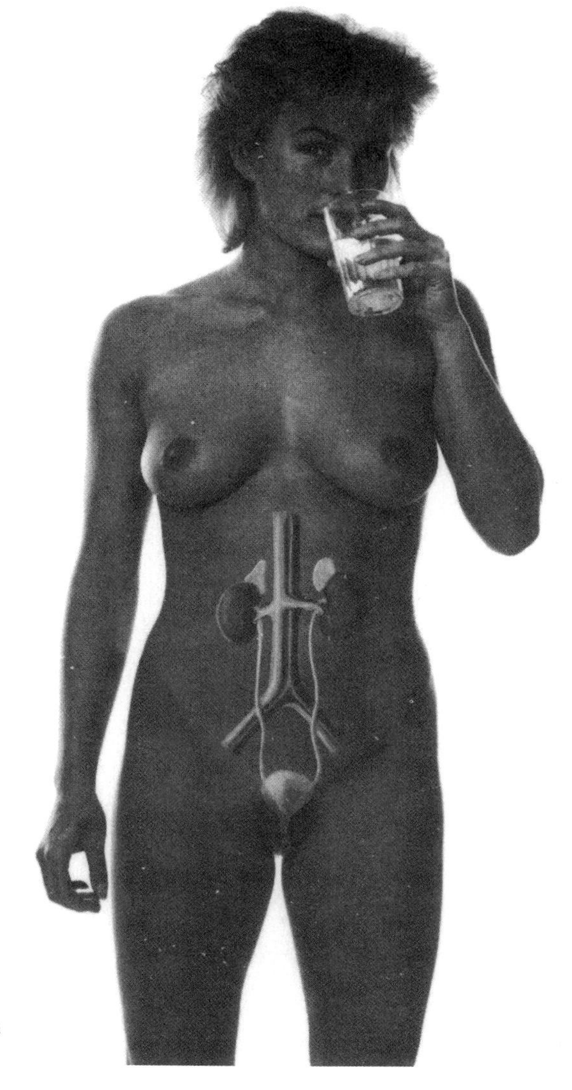

3 What substances does urine contain and how much urine is normally excreted during a twenty-four hour period?

4 Study the illustration of the kidney in the textbook. Which main structure can be identified in the kidney?
Label the illustration.

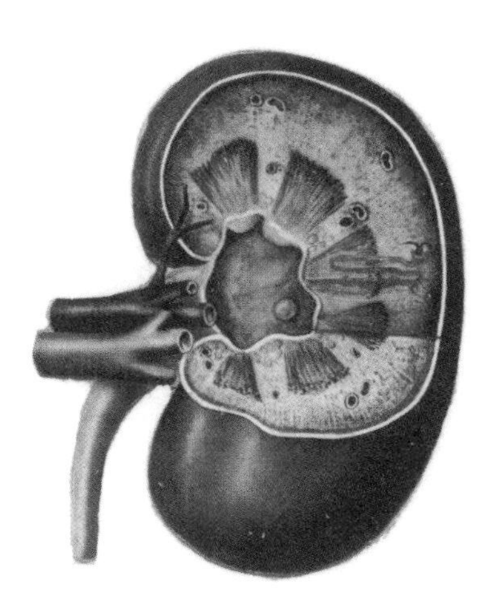

5 a What is a nephron and how many nephrons are there in a kidney?

b What is special about the arteriole in Bowman's capsule when compared to the capillary networks elsewhere in the body?

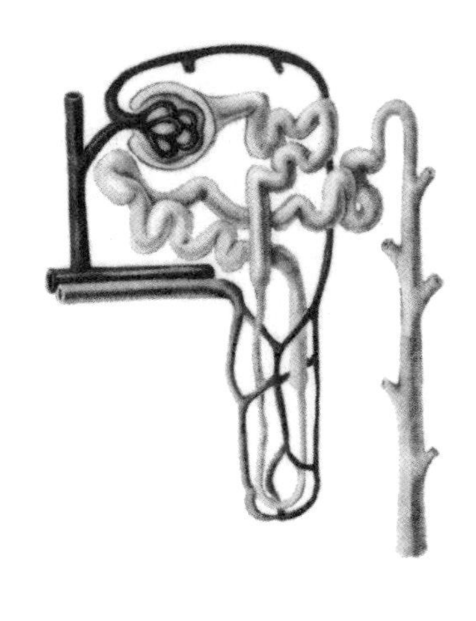

6 a What is primary urine and where is it produced?

b How much primary urine is produced every twenty-four hours?

c What substances does primary urine contain?

d Explain why primary urine does not contain blood cells or large proteins.

7 Where in the nephrons does the resorption of water from the primary urine take place?
How much water goes back into the blood every twenty-four hours?
Which other substances are reabsorbed into the blood when this happens?

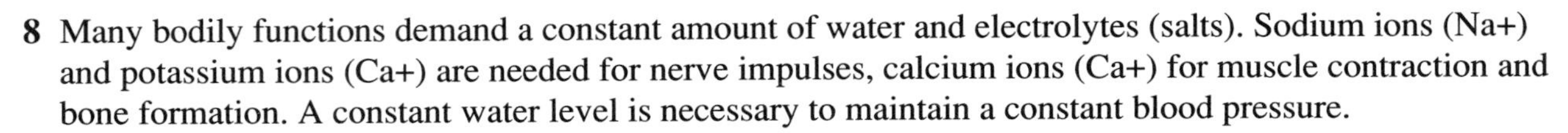

8 Many bodily functions demand a constant amount of water and electrolytes (salts). Sodium ions (Na+) and potassium ions (Ca+) are needed for nerve impulses, calcium ions (Ca+) for muscle contraction and bone formation. A constant water level is necessary to maintain a constant blood pressure.

a How does the body lose water and salts?

b How does the body gain water and salts?

c How is the electrolyte balance in the body maintained?

9 How do you know when your body needs water?

10 a What is ADH?

b What function does ADH perform in the body?

11 Explain why someone will be thirsty the day after he has drunk a lot of alcohol.

12 The pH value of the blood (the acid level) is normally 7.4. The pH value of urine varies between 6 and 8. How do you explain this?

13 Are the following statements true or false?

a When you drink little and perspire a lot, more ADH will be produced by the pituitary gland.

b When the blood pressure rises, more primary urine will be produced.

c Primary urine contains many proteins.

d The colour of urine is yellow because it contains few red corpuscles.

e The body produces approximately 180 litres of urine every twenty-four hours.

f Urine contains sugar.

g The kidneys regulate the acid level of the blood.

h The kidneys contribute toward the regulation of the salt level in the body.

i The kidneys participate in regulating the blood pressure.

True	False

The skin

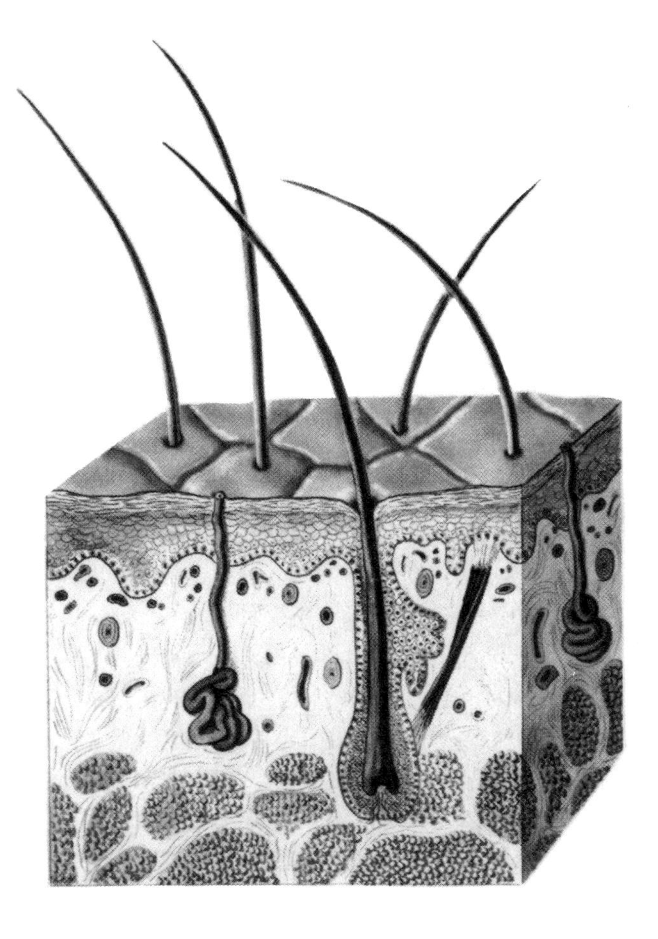

1 What are the main functions of the skin?

2 Label the various parts of the skin in the illustration.

3 The skin consists of three layers. Name these layers and briefly outline the differences in their functions.

4 How does new skin grow?

5 What is the function of the following:

   a sebaceous glands

   b sweat glands

   c hair?

6 What protection does the skin need from the strong ultraviolet rays of the sun? What are the advantages and disadvantages of sunlight to the skin?

7 What is acne?

8 a What happens when the skin gets burned?

   b What first aid treatment is given in case of burns?

9 Have you ever had a small wound on your skin? Try to remember and describe what happened as the wound healed.

10 What role does the skin play in body temperature regulation?

11 The skin is also involved in the excretion of body waste. How does this take place and which substances are excreted through the skin?

12 Are there usually bacteria on the skin? Are they helpful or harmful to the body?

13 Assignment
Inspect the sensitivity of various parts of the skin by using a pair of clean dividers (or something similar).
Find out how close together you can place the points while still feeling both of them on different parts of the skin (neck, shoulders, upper arm, fingertips). When this test is carried out, the subject should keep his/her eyes shut, while a fellow student applies the instrument. The subject should say whether he/she feels one or two points.
Try this a number of times in several areas to ensure that the subject is not merely guessing. What differences do you notice between different parts of the body and between subjects?

The skeleton, the joints and the muscular system

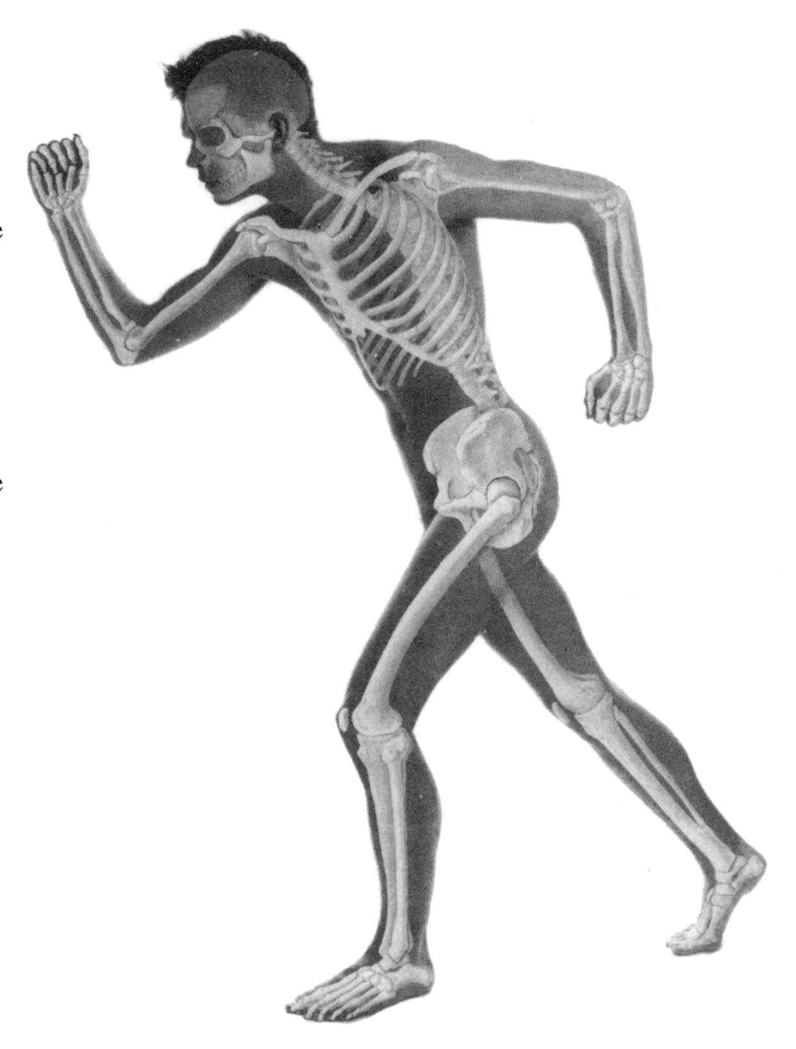

1 What would happen to the body if one of the following parts was missing?

a Skeleton

b Muscles

c Ligaments

2 Look at a skeleton carefully. Label the names of the major bones on the illustration.

3 Examine your own skeleton with your hands. Many bones can easily be felt through the skin. Which of the bones mentioned in question 2 are you able to feel?

4 **Assignment**
Dissolve a bone (eg. a small chicken bone) in a weak acid. The calcium will dissolve. Study the soft material that remains. What is it?

* **5** Look at a slide of bone tissue under the microscope. Describe the structure of the bone tissue.

6 How are bones classified?

7 Where is the red bone marrow located in long bones and what is its function?

8 What first aid is offered in instances of bone fracture?

9 Explain how bones grow in length.

10 a What is a joint? Give examples of the various main types of joints and specify where they are located in the body.

b Which type of joint allows for the largest degree of movement, and where in the body can these joints be found?

11 What are the menisci?

12 What are lateral ligaments?

13 What function do the spinal discs have? (You can feel a few by tracing your spine with one finger.)

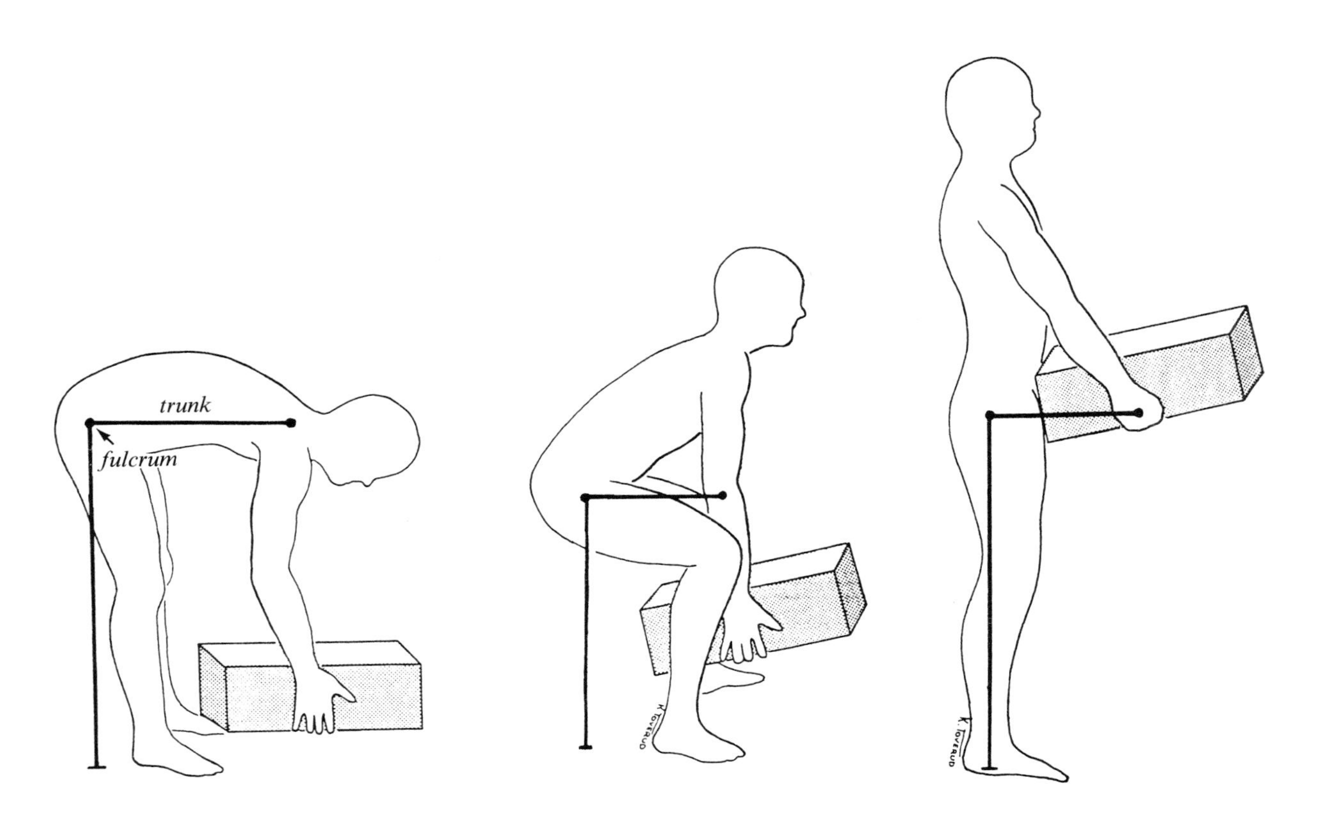

14 Assignment

When a person bends down to lift something, the upper part of the body (the trunk) can be regarded as a kind of lever, the hip joint being the axis (Fulcrum). The distance from the fulcrum to the place where the force operates on the lever is called the force arm. Look at the illustration. It shows both the correct and incorrect lifting techniques. To minimize back (lever) pressure, the force arm should be as short as possible.

15 a What is a flexor muscle?

b What is an extensor muscle?

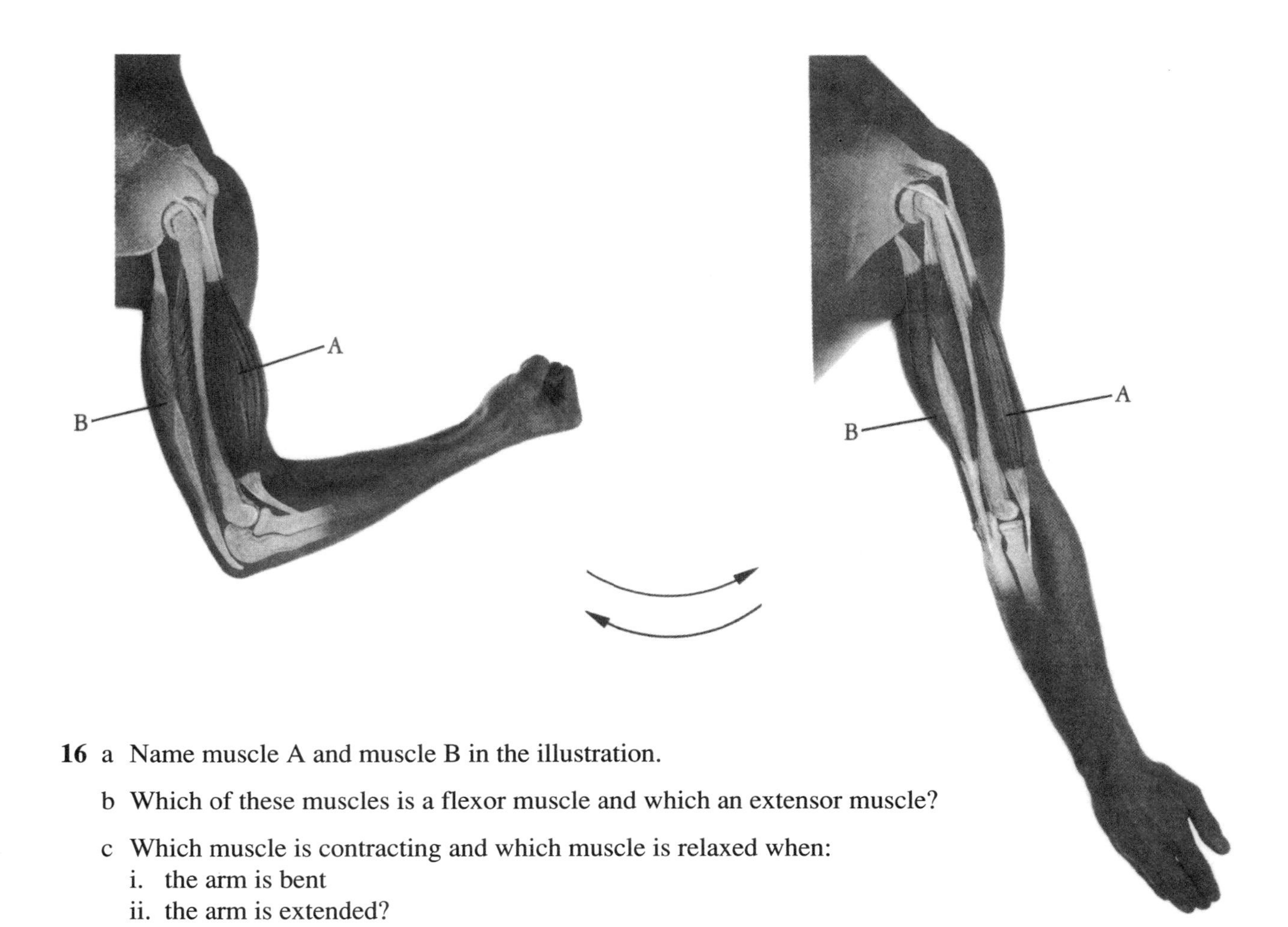

16 a Name muscle A and muscle B in the illustration.

b Which of these muscles is a flexor muscle and which an extensor muscle?

c Which muscle is contracting and which muscle is relaxed when:
i. the arm is bent
ii. the arm is extended?

17 What are natagonist muscles?

18 What are bursas? What is their function?

19 How many types of muscular tissue can you name? How can they be distinguished and where can they be found?

20 What is muscular cramp?

21 What measures can be taken to minimize injury to muscles used in maximal performance (ie. a top quality athlete)?

Puberty

1 a What is meant by primary sexual features?

b What is meant by secondary sexual features?

c Give examples of secondary sexual features of boys and girls.

2 Which substances trigger sexual development in the teenage years?

3 a Name the female sexual hormones. Where are they produced?

b Name the male sexual hormones. Where are they produced?

c At what age does the production of these hormones usually start?

4 What is the function of FSH (follicle stimulating hormone) and of LH (luteinizing hormone)?

* **5** What mental changes can take place during puberty?

The male sex organs

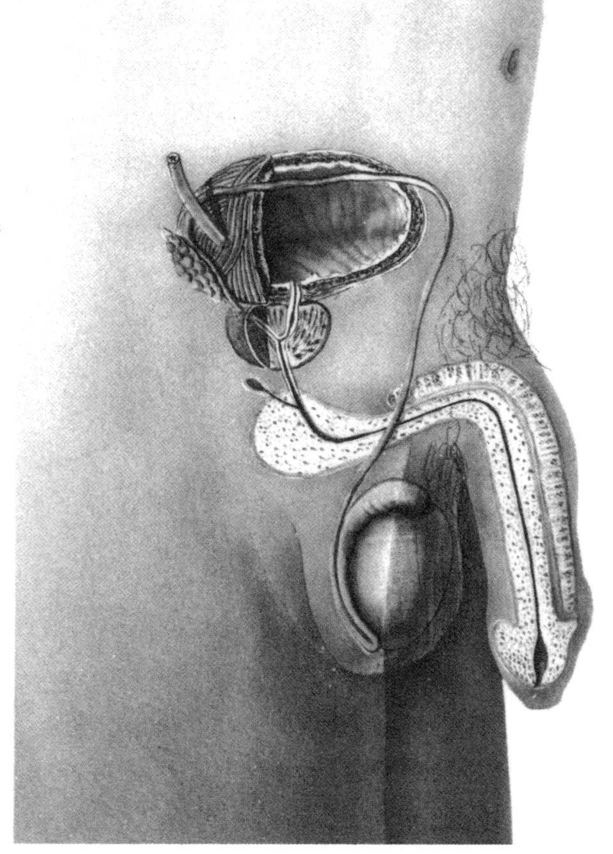

1 What are the main functions of the male sex organs?

2 a Name the various parts of the male sex organs in the illustration.

b Which parts belong to the internal and which to the external sex organs?

3 Study the illustration in the text book as well as a model of the male sex organs and answer the following questions.

a Describe the physical structure of the penis.

b What happens during sexual arousal?

c What is the function of the scrotum?

d What are the functions of the testicles?

e How does temperature affect the scrotum and testicles?

f Why is it important that the testicles lie in the scrotum before the onset of puberty?

g How many testicles does a man have and how are they constructed?

h What is the function of the seminal ducts?

i What is the function of the seminal vesicles?

j What is the function of the prostate gland?

k What are the functions of the urethra?

l What does semen consist of apart from sperm cells?

4 Explain the use of a condom as a contraceptive.

5 Older men often experience problems with urinating. Give an explanation of possible causes.

The female sex organs

1 What are the main functions of the female sex organs?

2 Label the component parts of the sex organs.

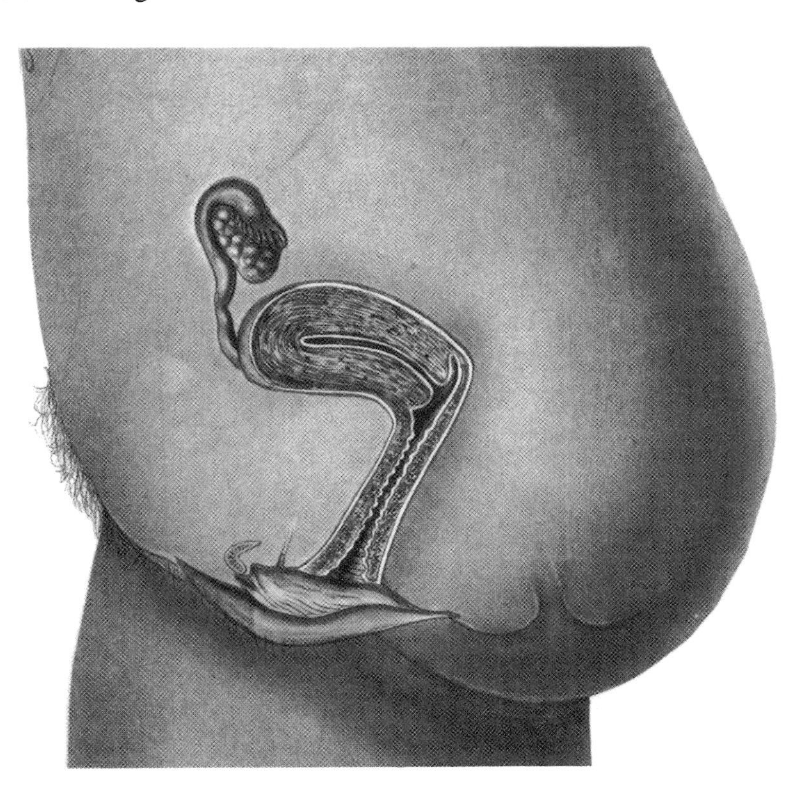

3 Study the illustration in the text book and also a model of the female sex organs and answer the following questions.

a What is the function of the ovaries?

b When are egg cells produced?

c When does the first ripening of the ovum occur?

d Where are the ovaries located?

e What is the frequency of ovulation?

f How many chromosomes does an egg cell contain?

g Where are the fallopian tubes located and what do they look like?

h How is an egg cell transported to the womb?

i What are the functions of the womb?

j What does the womb consist of and why is it constructed in this way?

k What is so special about the womb's mucous membrane?

l What does the vagina consist of?

m What are the vagina's functions?

n What is the clitoris?

4 How do the vagina and neck of the womb protect the internal sex organs against infections?

5 Which anatomical and physiological characteristics do the clitoris and penis have in common?

6 a How does the contraceptive pill operate?

b How does the mini-pill operate?

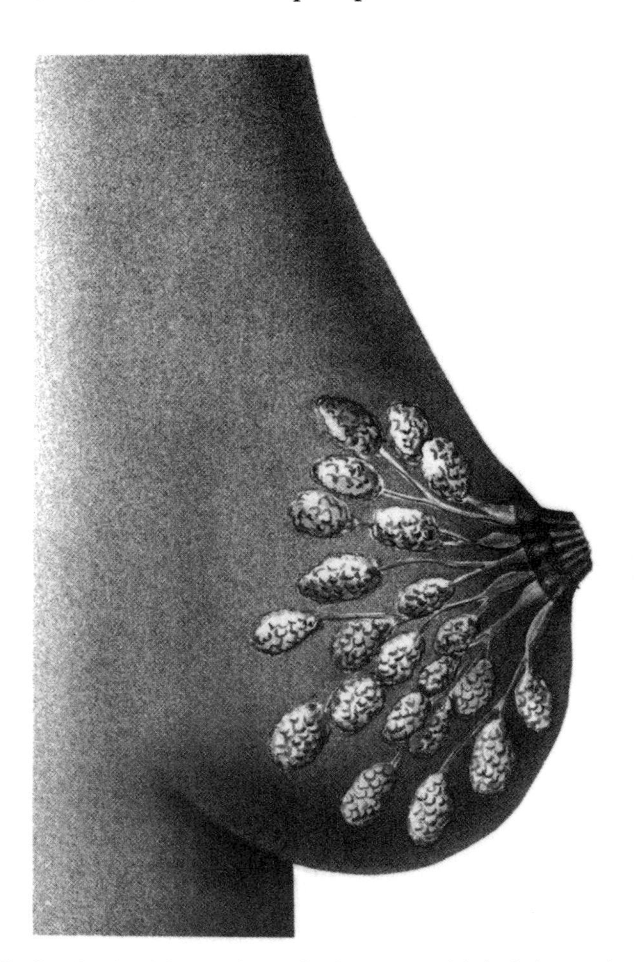

7 Study the illustration of a breast and label the various parts.

8 What are the sex hormones called which influence the development of the breasts?

9 What is the function of the female breasts?

***10** What are the hormones called that stimulate breasts into producing milk? Where are these hormones produced?

***11** The nipples contain many sensory cells.
In what way is milk production stimulated by suckling?

The menstrual cycle

1 What is meant by a cycle?

2 a How many days does a menstrual cycle last?

b What is the menstrual cycle a preparation for?
Briefly describe what happens during the menstrual cycle.

3 When does ovulation take place during the menstrual cycle?

4 Name the pituitary hormones that control the menstrual cycle.

5 Study the illustration in the textbook and make a survey of the coordination of the hormones during the menstrual cycle.

6 What is 'the yellow body' and what is its function?

7 When does menstruation (menstrual bleeding) occur and what causes it?

8 a For how many days (on average) does bleeding last?

b On average how much blood is lost?

9 a Why does menstruation sometimes cause mental instability?

b Which symptoms may occur as a result?

10 Why is good personal hygiene important in connection with menstruation?

11 a What is the 'change of life' and when does it start?

b What is the cause of this change?

c Why does this happen in women?

d How can women who are troubled by ailments during 'the change of life' be helped?

*12 The distribution of fat cells around the body differs between men and women.

a Can you name these differences?

b Which substances in the body control fat distribution and where are these substances produced?

Reproduction

1 What is the main aim of sexual intercourse?

2 a Why is foreplay important?

b What physiological changes take place during foreplay in men and in women?

3 What is an orgasm?

4 What is impotence?

5 During sexual activity diseases can be transmitted. Which sexually transmittable diseases can you name?
How can men and women protect themselves against these diseases?

Embryo and fetus

1 What is the most favourable time for fertilization during the menstrual cycle?

2 How does fertilization of the ovum usually take place?

3 What is a zygote?

4 a How long does the development of the human fetus take?

b How can the time of birth be predicted with great accuracy?

5 a Identify the three stages in the development of the fetus.

b Describe briefly the changes that occur during the three stages.

6 Why is there no menstruation during pregnancy?

7 At what stage during pregnancy does the formation of the external sex organs of the fetus take place?

8 a At what stage can the fetus sustain life outside the womb?

* b What is a child called that is born prematurely?

9 a What does the placenta consist of? Label the illustration.

b How are oxygen and nutrients transported to the fetus, and how is waste matter shed?

10 a Which hormones are produced by the placenta?

b What are the functions of these hormones?

11 a Explain how harmful materials can be transported to the child.

b When is the fetus most sensitive to harmful materials?

12 How does a pregnancy test work?

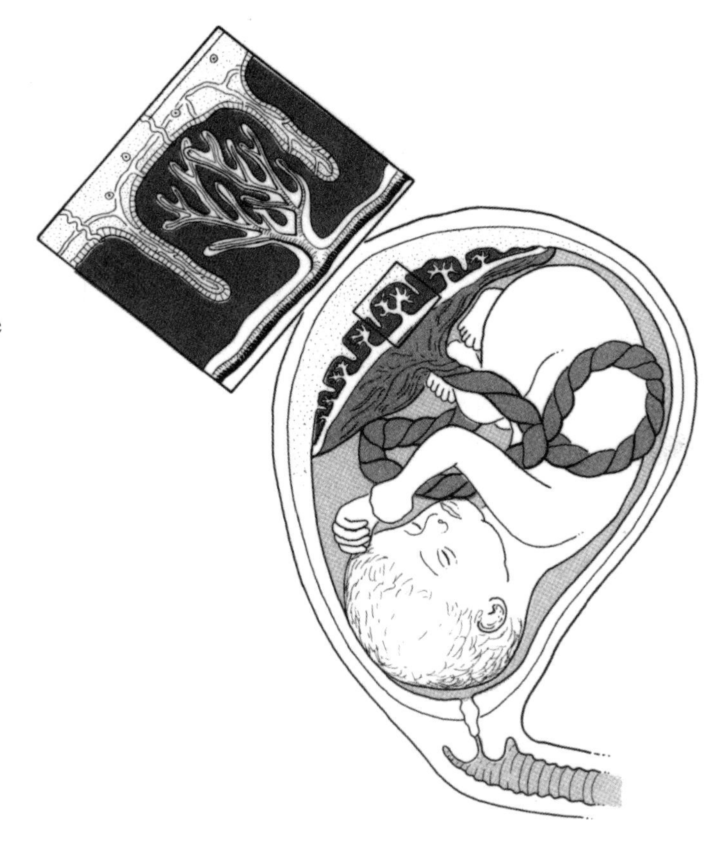

Pregnancy and birth

1 How long does a full-term pregnancy take?

2 a What are the physical signs that may suggest a female is pregnant?

b Which of these can be considered as unreliable and why?

3 a How much extra weight is usually gained by the mother during a pregnancy?

b What is the cause of this weight increase?

4 a How do breasts change during pregnancy?

b What is colostrum?

5 Why does the mother's volume of blood increase during pregnancy?

6 a Which nutrients are especially important for the mother during pregnancy?

b Why does the mother need more of these nutrients during pregnancy?

7 Give reasons why the fetus may be affected by the mother's state of mind (stress).

8 What are labour pains and when do they begin?

9 a What is the bursting of the membranes?

b Why does a future mother who wishes to give birth in hospital have to be transferred to the obstetric ward after the fetal membranes have burst?

10 a Name the three phases of childbirth.

b What happens during each phase?

11 a Why is mother's milk important and why is it good nourishment for a baby?

b What factors affect the mother's milk production?

c What may happen when the breasts aren't emptied properly?

12 a Why is good personal hygiene so very important in the period after the birth?

b How much time normally elapses after the birth before the womb resumes its original size and position?

13 When does menstruation resume after the birth?

14 What are the possibilities of another pregnancy happening during the breast-feeding phase?

15 Why is a child's first cry important?

16 Explain why the umbilical cord between mother and child may be cut immediately after the birth.

17 Discuss whether the atmosphere in a maternity ward has any significance for mother or child.

Heredity and environment

1 What is meant by heredity?

2 What do we actually inherit from our ancestors?

3 What is a gene and where are genes located?

4 What are X- and Y-chromosomes?

5 When you are a female, you received exactly half of your hereditary characteristics from each parent. How does this happen? What is the difference with a male?

6 a What is meant by a chromosome pair?
Look at the illustration and answer the following questions.

b How many chromosomes does this cell contain?

c How many chromosome pairs does this cell contain?

d How many chromosomes does each of the daughter cells receive after cell division (meiosis or reduction division)?

e Name the differences between the mother cell and the daughter cells after meiosis. Draw the chromosomes in the cells in the illustration.

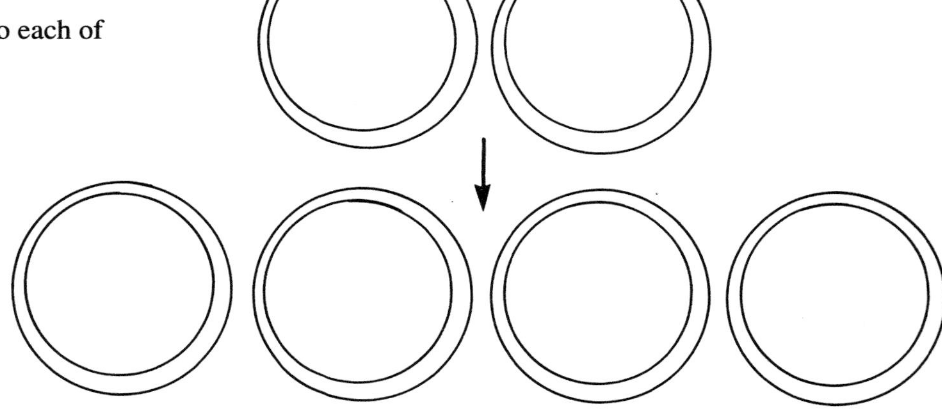

7 How many chromosomes do each of the following contain:

a brain cell

b sperm cell

c skin cell

d fertilized ovum

e ovum?

8 What is meant by a dominant gene and a recessive gene?

9 Assignment

Genetic factors among humans.

a Complete the chart with your own phenotypes and genotypes. The only tool that you need is a piece of PTC paper to taste from.

You are going to examine the distribution of the various easily discernable phenotypes and genotypes in yourself. Phenotype means characteristic that appears (brown eyes for instance) and genotype refers to the hereditary properties (genes) which an individual possesses as a characteristic. (BB or Bb, for instance, two genotypes which can both produce brown eyes, as the brown colour gene (B) dominates the one creating blue eyes (b)).
Dominant genes are in capitals, recessive ones in small type.
'B' means, for example, that the genotype is BB or Bb.

Characteristic	Phenotype	Genotype	Own Phenotype	Own Genotype
Sex	boy girl	XY XX		
PTC-tasting (rinse mouth afterwards)	is tasted is not tasted	T- tt		
Colour of eyes	brown blue	B- bb		
Tongue roll	rolls does not roll	R- rr		
Ear-lobe	free fixed	F- ff		
Hair-line	pointed straight	H- hh		

* Each strip has been impregnated with less than 0.1 milligrammes of PTC; students should not be allowed to sample more than two strips.

b Now use the genetic wheel below and find your genotype number on the basis of the data in the chart. Start off at the wheel's centre and follow the course outwards which corresponds with your characteristics and genotypes. Make a survey of the genotype numbers of the whole class. Do many have the same number?

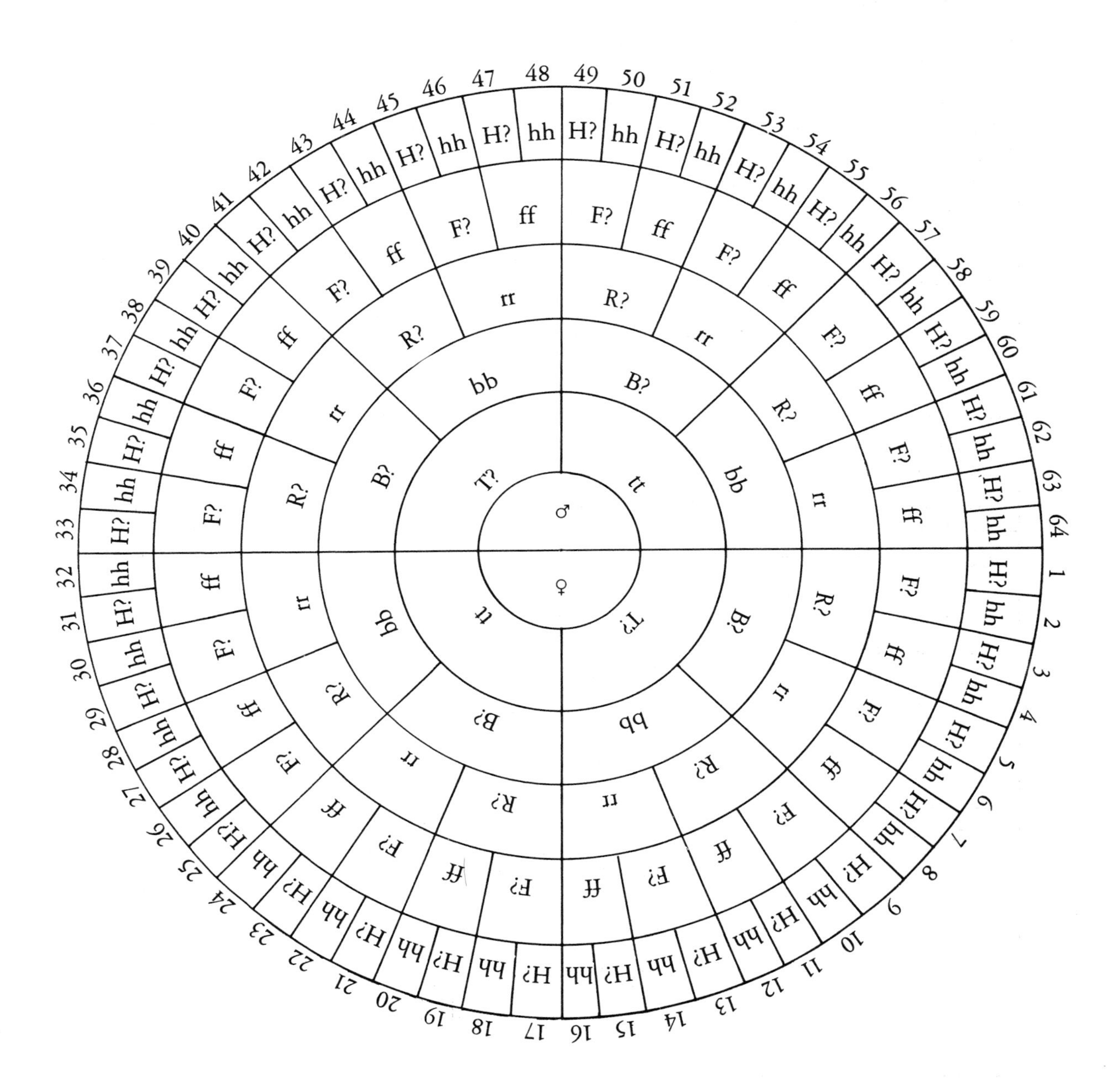

c In order to distinguish between those who have the same number, the test can be extended with the following characteristics.

This time supply the following chart with your own phenotypes and genotypes.

Characteristic	Phenotype	Genotype	Own Phenotype	Own Genotype
Hands folded	right thumb on top left thumb on top	D- dd		
Arms crossed	right arm on top left arm on top	A- aa		
Hair on middle phalanx	hair no hair	M- mm		
Bridge of the nose	straight uptilted	N- nn		
Freckles	freckles no freckles	S- ss		
Bent thumb	bent not bent	G- gg		

d Are there any students left with totally identical genes?

e Is it likely that two random individuals will have a totally identical genotype for all characteristics?

f Give an example of two people with identical genotypes.

10 Is intelligence hereditary? Give reasons for your answer.

***11** a What is a mutation?

b What can cause mutations?

***12** What is meant by sexually determined heredity? Give some examples.

13 A mother with blood group A gives birth to a child with blood group O. In a paternity case there are two possible fathers: one has blood group B, the other has AB. Can the father of the child be established with certainty? Can one of the possible fathers be eliminated with certainty?

Ageing phenomena

Ageing manifests itself differently from person to person. It is determined both by hereditary properties and by the individual's environmental factors. Environmental factors indicate how one has lived and lives.

Anne Johnston, 76 years of age, is a sane and sensible woman who likes to keep an eye on her health as much as possible. She enjoys being active and spending time with other people. However, during the last three years distinct physical changes have occurred which impede her movements and render her everyday life more difficult.

1 Changes in her eyesight have left their mark. She can read now with reading glasses but even with the glasses she can no longer do needlework which she used to enjoy very much.

a What might be the causes for Anne's failing eyesight?

b Make suggestions for aids or treatment.

2 Deterioration in her hearing has made it difficult for Anne to participate in conversation particularly when many people are talking simultaneously.

a What might be the causes for this deterioration of her hearing?

b Suggest aids that she could be given to help her hear more clearly.

3 Anne has always been proud of her skin. It used to be smooth and clear, but now it is wrinkled and flabby. What is the cause of this change?

4 For one reason or another Anne seems to get many small wounds. Bruises heal more slowly and tend to get inflamed.

a What might be the cause of the wounds?

b Why do they heal slowly?

c What is the significance of good personal hygiene to Anne?

5 Anne used to enjoy a daily walk. Yet her fear of falling increased with the years, and a walking-stick has now become her steady companion.

a What changes occur in the elderly regarding mobility?

b Why, despite her fears, does Anne need to remain active?

c What is the significance of a good balanced diet for Anne?

6 Mentally and intellectually Anne functions quite well. She has noticed, however, that she has become more forgetful with age.
Her grandchildren are surprised when their granny asks the same question several times over.

a What might be the cause of this?

b Why is it important for the elderly to remain both physically and mentally active?

c What is senile dementia?

7 a What might be the cause of poor blood circulation?

b Anne is receiving medical treatment for hypertension.
What could be the cause of Anne's hypertension?

8 a Why do elderly men sometimes experience difficulty with urinating?

b What might be the cause of urinating difficulties (incontinence) among women?

9 **Assignment**
Try to perform some domestic chores wearing dark sun-glasses.
Use ear-plugs while taking part in a group conversation.
Try to describe how you feel and what you experience in such situations.

Final assignments

1 Various body systems are involved in the regulation of the electrolyte and fluid balance. What are these systems and how are they involved in this regulation?

2 Blood pressure varies over a 24 hour period, however it is important that it does not get too high or too low.

a What can make it too high?

b What can make it too low?

c What body systems control blood pressure and how does it happen?

3 a What body systems are involved in the body's temperature regulation?

b Explain how these work to lower body temperature when it has risen too high.

c How does this system work to increase body temperature when it is too low?

4 Medical check-ups include blood tests. The amount of haemoglobin is measured as well as sedimentation. Why are these tests used and what do they measure?

5 Urine analysis involves the measurement of blood, protein, glucose and the pH-value. Samples are also screened for germs.
Find out what these tests might prove.

6 a What is a vaccine? Explain what happens when a person is vaccinated against a disease.

b It has proved difficult to develop a vaccine against the cold virus and the HIV-virus, but effective vaccines have been developed to combat smallpox and polio.
Why are some viruses harder to combat than others?

7 When a person is engaged in strenuous muscular activity, such as running, changes in the activity levels of a number of body systems are necessary in order for the individual to continue for any length of time. List these changes and explain what is happening with the body.

8 When an individual experiences sensations like anger and fear, changes occur in the activities of a number of organs and organ systems in the body.

a What changes take place and how are they brought about?

b Where do these changes occur?

c What correspondence do you find between these changes and those that occur when people exert themselves physically?
Try to explain this correspondence.

9 a What is noise?

b Give some sources of noise.

c Find out whether noise, apart from causing hearing defects, can be detrimental to health in any other way.

d Why is it important to protect oneself against excessively loud or continuous noise?

e How can people protect themselves against noise at work and elsewhere in society?

10 a What is glaucoma? What is a cataract?

b What are the symptoms of these two eye diseases and what treatments are available?

11 a What is meant by a psychosomatic illness?

b List examples of such illnesses.

c Explain why these illnesses may have psychological causes.

d How can psychosomatic illnesses be prevented?

12 How do alcohol and other drugs affect the various organs in the body?

13 Find out what mutations are and what they can lead to. Also sort out which factors might be conducive to the occurrence of mutations.

14 List information on hereditary diseases.

15 Discuss the impact of toxic materials on the environment and the human being in both the short and the long term.
Discuss some of the various pollutants which are discharged into the atmosphere or rivers, additives in foodstuffs, cigarette smoke, pesticides in agriculture, various medicines and other materials whose effects you would like to investigate further.

16 a What is the impact of radiation on the human body? Collect information on the potential dangers of radiation.

b Why is the emission of radioactive materials in nature so dangerous to animals and humans, even when the quantities discharged are extremely small?

17 Mrs Jones and Mrs Peters both give birth to a son on the same day in the maternity ward of the same hospital. After they arrived home from hospital it occurs to them that the babies may have been accidentally swapped in the Hospital. Blood tests are taken to discover whether this is indeed the case. Mrs Jones has blood group B, Mr Jones blood group A and baby Jones blood group O. Mrs and Mr Peters have blood group B and baby Peters has A.
Have the babies been switched? Support your answer with facts from the heredity and genetics texts.

18 Carol Stevens claims that David Williams is the father of her child. She insists on a maintenance allowance from him, but he denies paternity. The case is taken to court and the blood groups determined. Carol Stevens has blood group B, David Williams has O and the child has O. What is your verdict?

19 Explain how the body tries to prevent micro-organisms from entering the tissues. This is called the body's exterior defence mechanism.. Think of organs like the skin, the bronchial tubes, the digestive tract and the urinary passages. Explain how the body systems stop germs, viruses and other micro-organisms entering the body.

20 Use supplementary literature to find out how a nerve impulse arises and how it is transmitted from a nerve cell.

21 One of the functions of the pancreas is the production of the hormone insulin.

a What is the function of insulin in the body?

b What happens when the production of insulin is too low?

c Why do diabetics' kidneys secrete glucose in their urine?

d Explain why the following symptoms occur when there is a lack of insulin in the blood.
- increased thirst
- increased loss of weight
- increased frequent urination
- increased fatigue

e Why are diabetics subject to minor skin infections and capillary diseases?

f Explain why a diabetic who injects with insulin has to be very careful in his/her eating habits.

g Why do diabetics tend to keep sugar lumps in their pockets?

h What is a hyperglycaemic coma? What is a hypoglycaemic coma?

i Explain why it is more dangerous for a diabetic when the insulin concentration in the blood suddenly gets too high rather than too low.

22 There is a stable energy balance when the intake of energy (food) equals energy consumption. When the energy supply from food is greater than energy consumption, the remainder is stored as fat.

a List ways in which you can reduce your energy surplus.

b What can a positive energy balance lead to in the short and long term? List the possible consequences of obesity for an individual.

c What happens when energy absorption in the body is less than energy consumption?

d Which foods are still vital to the body even when a person is trying to slim? Explain why these foods are so important to the body.

23 The function of the parathyroid gland is the production of parathormone (PTH), which is important for the regulations of calcium in the body.

a What happens when the production of PTH ceases?

b What are the functions of calcium (Ca) in the body?

c Why do patients get cramps as a result of a lack of calcium?

d What will happen if there is an overproduction of PTH?
What may be the consequences for the patients concerned?

e Why is vitamin D important for the human body?

24 Heart infarct is a common heart disease and a significant cause of death in Europe. The illness usually hits patients who have suffered spasm of the heart (angina pectoris) at an earlier stage.

a What is a heart infarct?

b What happens to the arteries in cases of arteriosclerosis?

c Why can hardening of the arteries lead to heart spasms?

d Explain how the various risk factors may contribute toward the development of heart diseases.

e How can cardiovascular diseases be avoided?

25 The damaging effects of alcohol are extensive.

a What is alcohol?

b What is meant by permillage in the blood?

c What happens to the body when alcohol is consumed?

26 How does an excess of alcohol damage:

a the liver

b the digestive tract

c the brain cells

d the nervous system

e our general state of health?